The Weight of Words

Edi

D0582329

30128 80090 920 9

© Copyright 2003, Emma Fulham

First published in 2003 by
Tiger Claw Books on behalf of
The Emma Fulham Poetry Book Appeal.

All rights reserved. No part of this publication may be reproduced, stored in a retrieval system, or transmitted, in any form or by any means, without the prior written permission of the publisher, nor be otherwise circulated in any form of binding or cover other than that in which it is published and without a similar condition being imposed on the subsequent purchaser.

ISBN 0 9545847 0 8

Printed and bound in Great Britain by
Technical Print Services Ltd., Nottingham.
Cover design by Jon Perry.

Any views or opinions expressed in the book are solely those of the author and do not necessarily reflect those of the Editor or the Emma Fulham Poetry Book Appeal.

emmfpoems@hotmail.com

Tiger Claw Books
89 Station Rd
Balsall Common
CV7 7FN
Great Britain

The Sponsors of 'The Weight of Words' Were:

Allsopp & Co. Solicitors
The Balsall Common Lions Club
Golley Slater Brooker Advertising
The John Laing plc. Charitable Trust
John Shepherd Surveyors and Estate Agents
Kenilworth Round Table
The Lenton and Wortley Hall Association, at
The University of Nottingham
Leofric Lions Club, Coventry
The Lillie C Johnson Charitable Trust
Malcolm Hawkesford Estate Agents and Surveyor
Peter Clarke & Co. Chartered Surveyors
Robert Powell & Co. Chartered Surveyors and
Estate Agents
The Rotary Club of Kenilworth
Solihull School
Vaughan & Co. Estate Agents and Valuers
The Welconstruct Community Fund

Acknowledgements

I would like to thank the following people for their support, without which the book could not have occurred:

Rhian Lovell for her inspiration and enthusiasm, Peter Hewitt and Tony Dunn, for proof-reading, Rosemary Chapman for proof-reading and encouragement, David and Richard Reeves for their advice and guidance. Also Sue Neville for help above and beyond the call of duty, and Rosie Hewitt whose love and support I treasure and hold dear.

I would also like to thank my friends and family who stuck by me through my illness, and never let me give up hope.

Contents

Biography: A Day in the Life of a Bulimia Patient
by Jasmine

Introduction

It is at times a terrifying thought that Planet Earth is the only planet in the whole of the universe to harbour life. Even more extraordinary is that among all life on earth, human beings seem to have excelled all other living creatures in survival, creativity and imagination. The human race also stands out in the expression of a variety of emotions, such as love, hatred, compassion, anger, fear and aggression.

We experience a variety of life events from our birth on this planet to our death. It is a journey which has to deal with conflicts, losses and rejections, and this experience contributes to the way we are as persons and how we interact with our fellow human beings and the environment.

One of the life experiences which touches most of us is when we are unwell, either mentally or physically. Sharing the experience of such an event in life with fellow human beings is not easy. At times, words are not enough to reflect the real underlying feelings, thoughts and emotions which are associated with such an experience. Expression can take various forms, including music, painting, and writing. Fellow human beings are in debt to their colleagues who have shared their experiences which not only provide us with insight and understanding of such an experience but also gives us courage and strength to cope with adversity.

"The Weight of Words" does this exceedingly well.

Dr A JAWAD SHEIKH
Consultant Psychiatrist
Solihull Hospital

Foreword

By Emma Fulham

How the Book Began:

The idea for the book first came to me when I was recovering from an eating disorder, and wrote vast amounts of poetry, during sleepless nights. One of the rooms in the hospital had a selection of poems framed on the walls, and when reading them I was overcome with an immense sense of déjà-vu, it was as if *I* had written them, they were the same thoughts, feelings, and emotions I had been struggling with and expressed myself. This was combined with a sense of reassurance that these people had also faced the same battle in the same room, but ultimately recovered and moved on. It occurred to me that it would be an amazing thing if there was a book of poems that sufferers and their families could read.

The Authors

The poems came from a range of authors from all sections of the community. Letters were sent out to many hospitals with eating disorders units, self-help groups, and a request for poems and biographies was put in the Eating Disorders Association magazine. Word got round the hospital and poems started being slipped under my door. After several months or so I had over two hundred poems from fifty authors, male and female, and from all social backgrounds, ages, ethnic groups and religious convictions.

This was reduced to the forty or so authors and eighty six poems you will find in the anthology. Yet for the fifty people that sent me work there must be thousands whose poetry lies shamefully hidden away in diaries and on scraps of paper. Some of these people have always written, and some, such as myself have not written poetry since recovery. Some of the poems were written for the book, but most were works that had been written in private.

It is also important to note the spirit in which the poems were sent, that is that most were sent specifically with the aim of helping someone else. One of the most humbling things I found in the process of compiling the book were the letters that accompanied the poems. Many authors said they would not wish anyone to suffer in the same way that they were suffering, or as one author put it: 'I would not wish an Eating Disorder on my worst enemy'. Similarly, most of the letters said that they hoped my own recovery was going well, despite the fact that they had never met me. Indeed, the courage it must have taken to send those poems to me cannot be underestimated. This anthology is certainly unique in the way it presents a 'community' of sufferers, and (at time of publication) there is not a book I know of that contains such a vast number of sufferers. Furthermore, since sufferers of eating disorders become so isolated, and tend to 'lose' their voice, the book is significant in the way that it enables them to say to the world (albeit in anonymity) 'this is what we suffer with, this is the daily struggle we face...'.

Editing the Book

Several things need to be noted about the process of editing this book. Firstly, for reasons of confidentiality, first names only have been listed as authors' names, and in some cases complete anonymity was requested. It was also necessary to remove any details that may have compromised the author's privacy, thus all names were changed for the biographies. All references to weight were removed since eating disorders can be highly competitive, and it would contradict the purposes of the book if a sufferer were to read a poem and think they had 'failed' and were still 'fat', 'lazy' or had 'nothing wrong' with them because they had not dropped to the same weight as another author.

The Aims of the Book

The book is not intended to be a collection of new masterpieces, but rather to provide support and education. The book has been printed independently with donations from various businesses and charities, so it is only right that any profits not used for the reprinting of more copies will be donated to an eating disorders related charity. The aims of the book are:

1   To provide comfort and support for sufferers.

2   To demonstrate the everyday realties of living with an eating disorder, as expressed through poetry and biography.

3   To offer sufferers an example of a less destructive way of expressing emotions.

Why Poems?

Poetry is unique in the way that it allows a writer to enter into a stream of consciousness that writing prose does not, since the author is unhindered by the usual laws of language and grammar. Thus it seems to provide many people with a form of cathartic relief that other writing does not.

Why Biography?

The book was later expanded to include short biographies since this form of prose depicts the cause, evolution, and recovery from an eating disorder that poetry cannot.

The Thinking behind the Layout.

The poems have been carefully put into sections that roughly correspond with the recovery process that one hopes a sufferer goes through, realisation of the illness, expression of the feelings at the depth of the illness, and finally recovery. That said some of the poems written in the first chapter were written retrospectively, when the author has accepted they have a problem and has begun to look at the issues that caused it. The poems in the second section may at first glance make for difficult reading, until one realises how significant it is for a sufferer even to accept that they have a problem. After all, most sufferers silently struggle for months, even years in denial before acknowledging their problem. So what appears is simply the writing of someone that has 'bottled up' emotions for a long time, and is starting to learn to deal with them. Also included is a section of poems written by and for friends and family (or 'carers', as they are sometimes known). Sadly the carers are often the forgotten parties in a battle against an eating disorder, and the amount of distress that they also go through. Similarly, the inclusion of sufferers' poems to their family demonstrates the guilt and confusion frequently felt at the other end.

What Can the Poems Tell Us about Eating Disorders?

The poems provide perhaps the most accurate depiction of the everyday struggle of someone suffering from an eating disorder, whether anorexia or bulimia. The most common themes to appear are the struggle with obsessional thoughts, the lack of control over the illness, the depression and isolation felt, a low self-esteem and confused feelings towards the illness. Indeed, one of the most striking things about the poems is the change of metaphors that occurs within the different sections. During the depths of the illness the eating disorder is often referred to as a 'friend', something that still appears to provide a useful purpose in the sufferer's life. However, when the person has reached the stage of wanting to recover, the illness starts to be seen as something destructive and so the adjectives depicting the illness are more negative, such as 'enemy' or 'devil'. Occasionally, both positive and negative images occur together, representing the confusion and contradictory feelings felt. Other themes that are repeated are the disruptions caused to the sufferer's life and relationship, the fears about recovery and hospitals, and the desire to be understood. Some of the poems at the end of the anthology are distinctly optimistic, and acknowledge the positive aspects of the recovery process and life after an eating disorder.

Sufferers as Creative People.

Sadly the presentation of sufferers tends to be negative, both in its representation of the sufferer, and of their success in beating the illness. Too often stories focus on the weight a sufferer dropped to; ignoring the obvious fact that (aside from the physical risk the low weight poses) it is only a symptom of what an eating disorder is really about. In my experience (and I too have to generalise here) sufferers of eating disorders are sensitive, caring and creative people. The other sufferers I met during my illness may not only have written poetry, but had incredible imaginations and were fantastic musicians and so on. Nor need an eating disorder be a curse that forever taints the sufferer's life. Happily, society contains many people who have recovered and are quietly continuing their lives. I myself, would have preferred not to have suffered an eating disorder, but am grateful for the things I learned, the awareness I gained, and way I developed as a person.

Emma Fulham, May 2003.

This book is dedicated to those
who cannot yet
see the end to their struggle
against an eating disorder.

Elizabeth's story

I have lived with Emataphobia (fear of vomiting) since a traumatic experience of food poisoning at the age of four paralysed me with a fear for life.

At seven my parents divorced, and I started at an extremely academic, highly pressurised school; where eleven years of bullying commenced. At this time every decision was motivated by fear. I refused to eat any food that might make me sick, wouldn't go to restaurants and avoided people who were ill, just in case. This avoidance behaviour was interspersed with horrendous panic attacks that could strike at any time, in addition to OCD (Obsessive Compulsive Disorder.) As you can imagine, my life became very restricted.

Everything came to a head when I was thirteen and I stopped eating. After years of pretending that I could cope with the divorce and constant bullying the denial ended and I literally broke down. I was petrified that I was going to be sick. Twenty-four hours a day were spent on the sofa either in hysteria from panic, or relentless weeping. I remember envying everyone else for being 'normal', but I felt so far removed from any human being that no-one could reach me; I couldn't even see my loving, distraught parents.

My weight fell dangerously low. Convinced the churning sensation in my stomach must be illness, I went to the doctor. Baffled, he referred me to one of the top gastroenterologists in the country, for whom I put on an Oscar winning performance. I managed to convince this man, who was more than well versed in his field, that I may be seriously ill. The words 'stomach' and 'cancer' were bandied around. By this time I was convinced I had cancer too, and when a date was arranged for an Endoscopy (a camera in a tube passed down your stomach through your throat) a procedure that would surely make me vomit, I wasn't sure if I wanted to live.

My survival instinct and the amazing support from my parents saw me through this ordeal. The results were clear: it was stress, a nervous breakdown, which culminated in Anorexia. Everyone breathed a sigh of relief, but for me it was only the first step along a traumatic and life-long recovery. Months of psychotherapy saw me gradually eating and slowly my way of thinking began to change. I felt hungry for the first time in a year.

I had to repair all the damage that negative brainwashing had done to me, thoughts such as '*I am hideously ugly*', '*I must be an embarrassment*' or '*I'll only be liked if I am perfect all the time*'. I felt as if I was struggling for my foundations, a niche not only in my life but also in society and had thoughts like: '*Am I important?*', '*where do I fit in?*'.

The answers to all these questions were found in being at peace with myself. **Acceptance** – the one thing I had been scared others would not give me. They did, with unconditional love, support, and total confidence. I realised that I am what I am; I am allowed to like me, I accept me, I forgive me, I am just as I am meant to be. I found my power.

I believe that everyone has this strength. The key is to find all the destructive blocks that prevent you from enjoying all that is rightfully yours, and you are half way to freedom.

I am writing this as a twenty-year-old, in the hope that sufferers of eating disorders can take courage from my story. I still live with my phobia and '**live**' is the word. I truly love life. From this experience I am privileged to have greater empathy with and understanding of others. It has shown me where my true strength lies.

At the time of writing it is far from over, but now I go for months without panic attacks, and I eat a variety of different foods in a wide range of places. I can be around people who are sick without the fear of losing control. I am able to face each day confidently in the knowledge that I am strong enough to survive all that life gives me. My journey to this point has taught me more than I could have dreamed of. I was far from alone. So many of us suffer in silence, ashamed and embarrassed.

I was once asked what advice I would give to someone suffering from an eating disorder and it would be this: be truly sure that you want to get better, take courage and you **will** do it. Keep enjoying all that this wonderful life can offer you, forgive yourself and keep healing. There is light at the end of the tunnel; it's yours for the taking when you are ready.

CHAPTER 1

The Beginning of the Illness.

Changed Person

I know that I have changed so much
From the way I used to be,
From the very outer person
To the deepest inner me.

Before I was so loud and proud
Happy and carefree,
That was before my life was taken over
And my problems got to me.

The new person is such a mess:
So insecure and weak,
Finding the old person
Is whom I have to seek.

Leanne

Flashback

The strength of the flashback leaps across my heart.
Vision of:
Three girls on a platform
Hugging each other tight.
Only pain and loneliness in this time warp,
Me crying alone in my bedroom.
You said missing you was a burden
A feeling so solitary, tinged with jealousy,
A friendship golden-eyed, I wanted to flourish.

How will I cope on my own?
Fine – I should think.
I didn't expect these feelings to return from the sink.

How would others view this situation?
Now I've made so many new friends,
Overcome this illness
Dad says I'll be even stronger again.

Perhaps I want to scream your name to the stars.
Embarrassment would stop me: that you,
One hundred miles away might hear.
Perhaps I'm just too tired.
Each day I croak '*I'm a wonderful person*'
Today seems harder than the last.

Emily

Night on the Town

'Are you anorexic?'
Jeering and laughter
While juddering of nightclub music
Thuds at my heart.
How could they say that so publicly?
I had not the skills to quieten the jokes.

'Or an anorexic that likes to make herself sick?!'
More sneering.
'Shh!' and quietly spoken,
But giggles in surround sound.
'No. I'm not.'
I know I'm lying in part.
Makes herself, *makes herself* – as if for fun.
No clue of painful unhappiness behind that pun.
Quick. Think. How do I react?
Mission aim: retreat by saving face and
Denying knowledge of illness.
That illness that is a 'failing'.

So let us make a joke of it:
'Who me?'
Laugh and pretend,
They've no idea of this dead end.

Anonymous

Where Did It Come From?

Where did it come from?
Where did it start?
Where are the answers
That will help this depart?

I'm faced with a battle
Both day and night
I feel so frightened
As the end's not in sight.

There are good days and bad days
Steps forward and back
As I fight with my feelings
Caught up in a trap.

Coping is hard
And recovery is long
But finally I realise
That all this is wrong.

As I walk forwards
I never look back
Coping with things
I didn't think I could hack.

With the support of my family
And of my friends
I can see that my nightmare
Is reaching an end.

Anonymous

The Expert

The room is blue,
A Monet print hangs above the desk,
A musty smell lingers in the air.

'Do you mind if I light a cigarette?'
'No,' I say.

But I do.

My bottom perches on the edge of the chair,
Like a naughty parrot who's pulled out its feathers.

'So what's been happening?'
Is that medical language?
'I make myself sick', I say,
'So does that make me mad?'
He laughs.
'No madder than the rest of us'.
I search his blue eyes for signs of insanity.
My eyes flick across the room,
The expert's room.
I've never met a psychiatrist before,
Not sure what to expect.

My parents wait downstairs,
'*Jeeeesus!*' Dad says
Seeing skeleton No.3 wheeled past.

He doesn't say much, the specialist.
No profound words of wisdom.
He bites his nails, like a contemplative gerbil.
I'm missing Netball for him!

How dearly I'd hoped for a quick half-hour cure.
Perhaps that's in the second appointment.

Jasmine

The 'Other' Me

I look in the mirror but what do I see?
I know the person I'm looking at isn't really me
Once happy bubbly living carefree,
Now all I feel is everyone looking at me;
My confidence has gone taking my sparkle and shine
Just hug me and tell me I'm going to be just fine.
Why can't I wake up from this bad dream I'm in
And realise there's more to life than being stick thin?
I'm going to hold my head up high,
Battle with each day,
Because where there's a will there'll always be a way.

Mandy

Questions

Can't you tell me what's happening to me?
Why can't you unchain me and set me free?
Why do I ache and have a pain in my heart?
Why when life's so very short can I not make a start?
What's holding me up, what's keeping me here?
Why when I'm alone am I frozen by fear?
Why when with others do I feel so alone?
Why is nowhere secure, why is nowhere home?
Can't somebody tell me, who am I?
I feel so very misdirected and lost,
To try once again, how great is the cost?
Am I allowed to ask for that precious second chance?
To relearn the steps to this most complex dance?
Have you lost your patience, do I bore you?
To get your attention, what must I do?
Can't you see in my eyes the hurt that I feel?
To others a joke, but to me it is real.

Alex

Caroline's Story

It's very difficult to summarise the beginnings of my illness. The version I depict here is simplified, because it certainly takes a combination of events for anyone to become ill. Three to four years before writing this biography I was happy with my figure and would not have dreamt that I would ever develop an eating disorder. I never read women's magazines and my life had the normal human range of joys and sorrows. I had had a happy childhood, and a stable family background. In fact I was probably one of the masses who say: 'how can they do that to themselves?'.

My eating disorder developed as a reaction to a series of upsetting changes and disruptions that occurred in my life when I was seventeen, and which left me lonely, angry and depressed. When a friend died a few months after these changes I decided to regain my fitness by starting athletics, and as I saw it 'turn over a new leaf'. When I started cutting down on food nine months later, the need to exercise was based on the fact that I felt lazy and slow. I was constantly thinking how my old school-friends were doing 'x' hours of sport, whereas I had put on weight since my problems began. The memory of me comfort eating after my friend's funeral for example, became a torturous nightmare. Making a connection between my unhappiness and my weight was the final step on a slippery road to my eating disorder.

Slowly my unhappiness became centred on food. I started semi-dieting in the summer of my lower sixth, but by the autumn it became an absolute commitment. I was not seriously bulimic in the autumn term of my upper sixth: neither was I the stereotypical anorexic who ate an apple a day. I had to fill my stomach up and devised numerous No-Fat meals to achieve this: breakfast would be All bran and water, lunch a plate of vegetables and a jacket potato, for example. Another thing I tried was to tie a belt tight around my stomach so it would only take a little food to make me feel full. This did not work: much to my annoyance, the piece of string simply slipped down or broke!

I only have hazy memories of the autumn of my last year at school. I gave up athletics in about November, and for a few weeks before that I'd only been able to go after I'd binged and been sick. It was around this time that my eating disorder began to show more bulimic tendencies. I could never have told anyone at this point; I would have been completely ashamed and worried they might try and stop it. The bulimic tendencies were also a reaction to the fact my parents had started to notice my eating was abnormal, and so I pretended to eat meals I didn't want to have, and then made myself sick afterwards.

By January I was being sick once a day – one of my worst memories was of having friends stay with me and not being able to hug them – I just wanted them to go away so I could binge on the biscuits we'd made. I used to leave empty packets around at this time – as a sort of cry for help. I was hoping that some fairy godmother would come down and hug me and say '*I know what you've been doing and I'm not going to judge you - you can tell me exactly how you feel.*'.

31

It is so difficult to tell people what has been happening. Bulimia is an intensely personal and private thing, yet feels shameful at the same time. It is as I wrote in one of my poems to a close friend – being seen vomiting would have been worse than being seen naked. Yet, I would simply ring up my boyfriend, and crying, tell him what I'd done. Sadly it reached the point when he was only able to ask, '*how many times today?*'.

The 'fairy godmother' came in the shape of a psychiatrist from a hospital with a specialist eating disorder centre. Apparently I was 'seriously depressed.' and was put on antidepressants. Depression for me meant living in a permanent blackness: such as seeing no reason to live, being tearful, an aching heart; not wanting to socialise or see why anyone would want to talk to me, and not being able to think more than one day in advance.

When I was ill I frequently thought of a quote from Macbeth when he is utterly hopeless at the end of the play and sees no reason for life.

> *'Tomorrow, and tomorrow, and tomorrow*
> *Creeps in this petty pace from day to day.*
> *To the last syllable of recorded time…'*
> *(Macbeth, Act 5 Scene 5)*

Having an eating disorder is an isolating and lonely experience. As one becomes more depressed you feel that you are to blame for the problems in your life.

Depression is certainly a large feature of eating disorders, and is both a cause and a symptom. Sadly eating disorders have the highest number of deaths compared to all mental illnesses: a large proportion of which are suicides. Indeed two of my friends attempted to commit suicide whilst I was an inpatient. Both are pretty, sensitive and talented girls. Both, happily, have now recovered. Prozac lifted my mood for a short while, but in no way was it a miracle cure.

Once trapped in the clutches of an eating disorder its very easy to get into a downward spiral as your thought patterns become more disordered. Bingeing becomes easier from a physical point of view as your stomach becomes used to rejecting food. By Easter time I sometimes spent most of the day bingeing, and it would be sparked off for many different emotional reasons. Low weight also helps to maintain the eating disorder. I reached an extremely low weight for my height, and inevitably at that level you are continually fighting a battle where you binge simply through starvation. It was, in fact a miracle I ever took my A-levels since by the summer I was so fatigued that I couldn't concentrate on reading, and the only subject which received any real attention was English, since the plays I was studying were on video and I could lie down and watch them.

It is so difficult to put across how I felt at this point. Food certainly dominated my thoughts – every shop I drove past would have possibilities to buy binge foods. Once at home on my own I felt trapped and unable to go outside the front door. If people were in the house I felt angry if they stopped my binge, as well as ashamed and deceitful. I would memorise what people ate at lunchtime, quantity and fat content, then compare it to what sport they did and their size. All my dreams seemed to feature food: such as being presented with a buffet meal, have everyone staring at me, and not know what to do. Dreams where I planned what to cut down on, and dreams where I planned what to binge; then of course the dream where I had to wear a tag saying: '*This Girl is Bulimic!*' and everyone detested me. Anxiety levels also soar when suffering with an eating disorder – I remember having weekly panic attacks at this time.

Low self-esteem is certainly another major factor in eating disorders. It is easy to imagine the vicious circle when the bingeing cycle you are in seems to confirm what a dislikeable person you are. I found it easy to look around and wonder why other people have eating disorders – because you see the positive qualities in them – yet in the summer I could not bring myself to write a sentence to say what was good about me for the self-esteem homework my psychiatrist had set me.

After the blur of A-levels I began doing three days a week day-care at the hospital. It is a big help to know others are in a similar situation. I was amazed to talk to another day-patient and discover that the feelings and thoughts she had in her head were almost identical to mine.

Once at home however, things would fall apart, I would return to bingeing and compensatory behaviour. After the drive home I felt so tired and unhappy that I had no energy to try and move forward. I realised when on holiday at the end of the summer that I could only get better if I became an inpatient and had someone to help me through each mealtime. By this point I was making myself sick after everything I ate, around fifteen times a day. Indeed, it was actually a relief to escape the home environment when I was admitted as an inpatient in September. Family relations become very strained and it is extremely difficult for those with close emotional ties to try and help.

Being in hospital meant I no longer had to worry about what to do at mealtimes – I just had to eat what was in front of me. In the morning we would fill out a menu – a starch, protein, vegetable and pudding for each meal. You can gain a lot of support from having people there in the same situation (though it was a long time before I was able to openly say when a mealtime was difficult). One of the first big steps forward I made was when I went up a portion size and had people around to say that they'd experienced the same painful discomfort as me – and that it would pass. Sitting in my room that night determined not to be sick was a big step forward – it is a difficult feeling to suppress when your stomach has shrunk and all you need to do is tighten your stomach muscles to bring it up.

We had two to three groups each day, which included the following: dietician/nutrition group, relaxation, body image, psychotherapy, self-esteem, drama therapy, art therapy, anxiety management, and assertiveness. On Fridays we had a quiz, and creative group in the afternoon where you could do anything from glass painting to sewing. (Relaxing and enjoying yourself tends to disappear when you have an eating disorder.) There would also be a weekly meeting with your named nurse and psychiatrist, and I attended a bulimia group, which concentrated on working through specific weekly goals to get better.

Furthermore a Complementary Therapist was available to give a weekly massage. The importance of seemingly simple activities like this cannot be overlooked. When ill with an eating disorder the tendency is to cover up by wearing baggy clothes, and any sort of physical contact is limited. People tend to stop giving you hugs when you become very thin – I remember one of my friends saying she was scared my bones might break. The massage is slowly built up – starting one week with a hand or arm massage until the patient feels ready to move up a step. Clearly this would be even more difficult if one had suffered sexual or physical abuse. The aim is that massage will be a form of relaxation. Such massages also help to increase blood circulation, which is inevitably a major problem for someone who is starving themselves.

I had to keep a 'food and mood diary' for my Bulimia group. I had tried to do this whilst studying for my A-levels, but it only really became a regular thing, and a source of comfort when I became an in-patient. Indeed, to begin with it was little more than a record of how many times I had made myself sick each day, which was as much as fifteen, though I often lost count. Towards the latter stages of the group we also begin to tackle negative thoughts of all types by noting them down and challenging them. Initially I was only able to write them down and found it very difficult to challenge the automatic internal mental abuse I gave myself, but that slowly improved.

There are many other things I found helpful whilst in

hospital – receiving cards and letters from people letting me know that they care. Letters from friends at a self-help group I went to were especially touching. Equally important was the opportunity to break though the isolated world I was trapped in – allowing myself to tell someone I was having a bad day instead of hating myself for it. There were other small things that were similarly heart warming, such as when an occupational therapist made me a tape full of motivational and reassuring songs. Playing it in my room made me feel less alone. I also used to write down all the positive things that had happened that day; and along with some friends at a self-help group, I made a 'positive thoughts book' in which my friends wrote complimentary thoughts and inspiring messages that I could reach for at low times.

The fact that I asked to go into hospital was definitely a positive fact. It meant I was more prepared to work at getting better than if I had been put in six months before. I was as sure that I wanted to recover, as I was that I needed help in doing so. I knew that I'd a huge gap in my life where the bulimia would not be, and so I took in all sorts of hobbies I had not had spent much time doing before. I was determined that I would have something to distract my thoughts. And so I covered my wall with pictures, started learning to play the guitar.

Part of my motivation for writing this biography is to help people understand what it *really* feels like to have an eating disorder. Sadly, when I was very ill I was unable to stand up for myself when cruel comments were made. A friend at college completely ignored me when she realised

I was Bulimic: my one conversation with her about it consisted of her looking at me in disgust, curling up her nose and saying '*can't you just eat one biscuit and leave it*?!' This was a terrible thing to say because it confirmed some of the bad feelings I had about myself. That I was 'bad' for 'letting' the eating disorder take over my life, whilst I seemed unable to stop my obsession with food. It amazes me how ignorance can cause so much gossip. My boyfriend of the time was asked by someone from sixth-form college '*Are you still going out with that girl? I heard she'd been carted off to the loony bin!*' Far from it. My illness enabled me to meet some of the nicest people I have ever met. It also allowed me time to think, learn and re-learn as well as recover.

I am convinced that many positive things came out of the eating disorder. As I look back on the illness it only seems to be a sort of journey that had to be undertaken for me to become the person I am now. It is as if I had to reach my lowest to want to begin to recover.

Since recovering I have felt happier, than I ever thought I could do and more independent and mature than I did before. I feel I know myself better and can appreciate, accept, and work on my strengths and weaknesses. I have also made many new friends from all walks of life. Eating disorders can make you a more sensitive person, and I am certainly more able to sympathise with all kinds of mental illnesses and addictions. The illness taught me how to be more assertive, and to discover many different ways of looking at the world and approaching life's problems. Having had an eating disorder doesn't need to be something that will hold you back, for me, it has been quite the opposite.

CHAPTER 2

During the Illness

Afterwards

That is disgusting:
What I just ate
Punishing myself
Can no longer wait,

Getting rid of the food
Is what I must do,
I really don't mind
What I put myself through.

I don't care if it's laxatives
Or making myself sick
However much pain
It's just got to be quick.

Jane

Another Day

Dawn has broken, another day is here.
Prozac's not working, the devil is so near.
The same obsessed thoughts are circling my head:
How much food today? It fills me with such dread.
How much will I eat?
How much won't I eat?
I must not let myself have any treats.
The laxatives are now starting to work,
Getting rid of all the bad is a perk.
The devil is in me helping to see:
The more weight I'll lose the less there'll be of me.
The good voice of the devil is within me,
I don't need food he's helping me to see.
I'm so fat I need to lose more weight,
I look disgusting, in such a bad state.
Time goes by and I feel so sad and alone,
I hear the voice, the devil's voice; it's bad.
'Come to me' he says and I go. I'm mad.
I let him take over – can't stop it,
Frightened and scared I don't like this one bit.
I feel so ashamed and I'm so angry,
I'm such a freak and worthless – why me?
I try to get help I'm in so much pain,
But the doctors don't wanna know,
I know the fight will be hard and long,
But I will make it; I want to be strong.
I won't give up, I'll fight until the end,
The devil won't win, I'll find my true friend

Anonymous

Angel

And what will you say?
I'm sorry for today?
My heart was melting,
I couldn't complain.
Were you there beside me?
Eating. Drinking. Sleeping. Loving.
    Breathing.
Are they just battles I cannot win?
I thought I was running towards the edge of life.
Did I trip and fall?
I cannot forgive myself at all.

My own world of warmth
So comforting,
    So protecting:
Surreal feelings I cannot replace,
Screwed up emotions have been ripped out of place.
So much to do, and see, and feel,
But I can only conceive taste and size,
size and taste.

I miss you I say.
You smile:
    'I'm always there but just for play'.
Is it that how it started, just a game?
To return in times of need, times of shame?

I thought I'd bred many things to keep me strong.
At home Bulimia stabs me in the back;
  And tries to prove me wrong.
All those weeks of work,
  And you return.
Return to think you want to bring it back.

It seems so unfair.
Why should I have that world I controlled?
Taken away from me?
They don't understand I feel I can never be free.
I was in so deep. A connection so strong
  My friend,
  My punishment,
A helping hand to absorb all the feelings.
Nothing can ever replace those feelings
      – don't you see?

I don't need anything else at home:
Food is my world
We have been wedded for over a year
I'm in a hazy path trying to steer me clear.

The intricacies of what to binge,
  When, why and how.
I don't need anything else – for now.

This thing and me,
We're closely attached
I'm so scared to let go
With shadows of unhappiness still in tow.

'I know'
        You whisper,
'I know.'

Jasmine

Anorexic World

The lies and conspiracy
The deceit and the pain,
Being anorexic
Is like playing a game.

Avoiding the food
In any way that you can
Making things up
To follow a plan.

The aim of the game
Is to lose lots of weight
To gain all the control,
To hide all your hate

Is what you get
Worth all that you do?
Suffering so much
With all that you go through.

Leanne

Being Here

Being here is harder,
Harder than I thought,
Doctors trying to preach to you
What they've all been taught.

Lots of time spent on my own
Not knowing how I feel,
Things going round in my head
Just like a magic wheel.

I dread every mealtime,
Being given lots of food,
Sitting there and playing with it
Trying not to be rude.

The groups are really scary
As I don't know what to say,
It's like joining in a game
That you don't want to play.

At least while I am in here
It gives everyone a break
A chance to set their limits
Of what they all can take.

Anonymous

Bulimia

Binge, Binge, Binge,
Ultimately sick.
Lies, Lies, Lies,
Isolation from the rest.
Many, many, problems
In the messed up little world
All that you can think of
Has really been disturbed.

Leanne

Carrying On

Another day,
Another lie,
More tears are shed
As I lie there and cry.

I feel a mess
In more ways than one.
I constantly question
Can I carry on?

One minute I'm normal
Acting happy and kind,
The next I am angry
Going out of my mind.

Controlling emotions
Is too big a task,
Carrying on with this illness
Is too much to ask.

Leanne

Chocolate Grocer

This is the small village shop
For the city-lot in the commuters' slot,
Watch them buying Western trash
Chocolate, crisps and instant mash,
See those filled to guts galore,
Not me, I vomit and return for more.

Ladies in red-white pinstripe uniform
Mirror the cuts with which my arm I adorn,
Blank routine serving confectionery supreme,
Look at all the colourful wrappers:
Two million grams of fat unclean.

Jasmine

Confusion

Why is it so hard
To explain how I feel?
No one understands
But the mess is so real,

I feel so unhappy about myself
To the point of destruction
Of my body and health;

I deserve all the pain
That I put myself through,
But how long can I take this?
I really don't know.

Sometimes however
I really don't care
I keep things to myself
That perhaps I need to share.

Sorting out these problems
Seems an impossible task
'Will I get through it?'
Is the question I ask.

One day these problems
Will be sorted out for good
But how much do I wish
That everyone understood!

Anonymous

Curl Up

If I curl myself up very small,
And hug myself tight
All the difficult feelings will be put to flight.
A loneliness I cannot explain,
My faltering heart squirms as thoughts race
                          through my brain,
I've had a bad day
If I curl up small
Will all the difficult feelings go away?
The door closes, the people go,
My bulimic thoughts are left to flow
These old thoughts seem there to comfort me:
If I binge – things will become easier,
                          you see?

I feel so scared to go out the front door
If I can make myself thinner
I can face the world once more:
Bony is fragile
So treat with care!
I can purge all those feelings away.
Get close to me – if you dare..

I have such trouble
Reflecting the idea people will like me:
Don't I deserve to be bullied and disliked?
They can inflict a pain I cannot do to myself.

My dictator starts up again:
'What are you doing? What have you done?
Make yourself sick – such a personal idea of fun.
You're feeling vulnerable
But if you're small
You won't be noticed – noticed at all'.

Anonymous

Daytime

Existence enters: unwelcome,
Compelling flesh into a screaming delirium
Of fear driven consciousness.
Sustaining poison
Breathes in my blood,
Hurting my heart.
Twisted and hideous,
My body shudders,
Pushed on by waves of degeneration,
Torn by mental aching,
Pursued by condemnation
Of self.
Bleeding from my eyes,
Desperation scratching at my soul,
I am pressed down by sickening fire
Into an imprisoning consummation
On future's bed,
It's love like tongues of torture
In a nightmare
Directed by day.

Tanya

Dear Bulimia

Shouldn't I be angry the Bulimia's not gone away:
And that I need to use two pieces of chocolate to
                          brighten up my day?
My boyfriend said: '*in the summer*'
I was '*painfully thin*',
What a nice controlled world
Where I didn't let others in.
Slim means immune from hurt,
Thin means shielded from pain;
Food is my universe;
The rest? The periphery.

Food glorious food,
Three puddings with custard
Swallow biscuits half-chewed
I'm in control if I have mustard.

One day I'll read this and see it doesn't make sense
Perhaps next year I'll be so strong
Food won't be my defence.

Please don't underestimate the powerful
Force driving the emotions,
Only my illness provokes these reactions:
Should I dispute the reality of my intentions?

Anonymous

Dig Deep

I pick up a knife
And look at my arm,
It's all my own fault
That I cause myself harm.

I'm cutting myself
– I can't believe this is real
But I know that it is,
Since the pain I can feel.

The next thing I know
My arms are a mess;
And so yet again,
I value myself less.

Anonymous

Do You Feel This Too?

Do you feel this too?
The gush of pain
Which threatens to drown me
With every breath I take,
Which pulls me down
So I have to fight
And cling to every hope.
Do you feel this too?

How many others have felt this way?
Have cried their tears or even worse:
Have held them back so no-one sees
The pain that twists and burns
A hole so deep inside;
How many more of you out there?

Does it ever end?
Can you tell me that?
Will Time 'the great healer'
Heal *this* pain,
And make me forget
Or make me smile?
Can somebody tell me,
Does it ever end?

Anne

Falling

You say that I am a beautiful thin girl.
Why can't I see what you see?
I just see a fat ugly girl
For once in my life,
Why can't I see what you see?

Falling.

Falling into my abyss of self destruction,
Deeper and deeper I fall,
I scream, but no one hears my cries for help.
I reach for something, anything at all.
I grasp the lifeline dangling there,
And then I realise I can get out of this:
It's going to take a lot of work,
But I will make it.

Anonymous

Fat

Fat Fat Fat
Is all that I am –
I need to be thin
But I'm not sure I can;

I've tried every method
Of losing the weight
But being fat
Just seems to be fate.

I know I'm obsessed
In more ways than one,
But I won't ever be happy
Until the fat's gone.

Michelle

Feelings

How do I cope with the feelings of dread?
With the out-of-control feelings filling my head,
Conflicts within me, raging continuously,
How will I manage? I just cannot see.

The struggle goes on, day after day,
My eating disorder has left me in dismay,
How did I ever get to this state?
But we all faced up to it before it was too late.

Sad, unsafe, lost and undeserving,
Panic, fed up, never belonging,
Guilty, fear and incompetence,
Angry, paranoid, totally unconfident.

All these feelings never seem to ease,
All my life, I've aimed to please,
My point of view never mattered,
I feel I've been emotionally battered.

So much pain and nowhere to go,
Is my eating disorder a friend or a foe?
It gave me strength I've always lacked,
It nearly ruined my life. And that's a fact.

Andrew

Food

Food,
Food,
Food,
Is all that I hear,
As I battle against
My greatest fear.

Wherever I turn,
Wherever I go,
Food is the topic:
But I don't want to know.

Cooking the dinner,
Going out for a meal,
No one understands
How unrealistic these feel:
I can't imagine
These things as a pleasure,
Being happy with food
Is a memory I treasure.

Leanne

Friday

Can I let you into a secret ?
I don't really like myself.
On Monday I was happy
Tuesday I started getting snappy.
The gloom has descended like fog once more,
That's when the insecurities return
        from the emotional store.

Yes, I've done many things
At a high level:
        not high enough for me.

Can I divulge a secret ?
I called someone today.
Said I'm unhappy with this self.
That's all that could be said – nothing else.

I'm braver and stronger than this.
I've been over worse.
And if the depths of depression
Lay in the valleys of the sea,
This would be a stroll down the Cotswolds.

Julia

Going into Hospital

Is going into hospital
As scary as it seems?
'Cos if I'm totally honest
Then I'm not really keen:

What is it they're going to do?
Is all I want to know,
Keep on feeding me
Until it's time to go?

Going into hospital
Means facing up to things,
Taking all the good and bad
That these few months may bring,

How will I feel
When I finally lose control?
No longer restricting what I eat
I suppose is the goal.

Going into hospital
Doesn't seem too real
I've lost all my emotion
And don't know how to feel,

When I come out
I don't want to be me
I want to be changed as a person,
Be totally free.

Leanne

Hospital Food

Sitting in the dining room
Are the worst times of the day,
I sit and look at all my food
And don't know what to say,

I know I cannot eat it
As I don't want to change,
The thought of putting more weight on
Is so scary and so strange.

So far I've avoided my enemy
By not touching it at all,
I doubt I can continue this
Because I know they'll make me fall;

Breakfast, lunch and dinner
They all get to me:
Stopping me from being
The person I want to be.

Anonymous

Lost

I'm lost in a space of negativity
Breathing my hostility,
Time is no friend for me,
Except to disappear continually.

There are two parts of me,
We talk and argue on issues – allowed for me.
My shadow and me wrestle continually,
Be translucent to your scenery.

I'm held back by my mental gravity
The negativity that is, in part, of me.

Tanya

A Day in the Life of a Bulimia Patient

I am twenty, and undergoing treatment at a specialist clinic for Bulimia and Depression.

My day begins at 8.00am when my alarm goes off and I lie in bed with my eyes closed until the alarm on my mobile phone goes off five minutes later: this is the one that actually gets me out of bed. Sometimes I am woken by a nurse bringing me my medication: an antidepressant. If they wake me they don't usually get a very good reception, though I try my best.

At 8.15 I run myself a bath and have a coffee, I usually lie there for about fifteen minutes; listening to the affirmations I've recorded onto tape, such as *'It is easy for me to change. I am flexible and flowing'* or *'I see all challenges as wonderful opportunities'*. The aim is to increase my self-esteem.

I now put on my moisturiser and go down to breakfast: a bowl of bran flakes and a slice of brown toast and jam. Margarine, because of its high fat content, still scares me so I avoid having that if I can help it.

Next I make my way to 'supervision'. This involves sitting down in a group with a nurse for an hour after meals to ensure we don't exercise or vomit up our food. There isn't always a nurse there but we sit there anyway. It's always very quiet with people filling in their menus for the next day. You tick a box for a choice of starch, vegetable, protein and pudding. The local radio station plays in the background, which gets irritating by the end of the day as they seem to play the same six songs on rotation!

At 9.50am I go down to the gym for half an hour's light aerobics led by an occupational therapist. I'm at a healthy BMI (body mass index) so I'm allowed to do gym. I'm on a slightly different programme to the rest of the EDPs (eating disorder patients) so I go to the gym every day. Most can only go twice a week, if at all. Two girls are at such a low-weight that it is dangerous for them to move about and are on 'bed-rest' i.e. they must remain in their beds. If they need to go anywhere they have to be pushed in a wheelchair. I wanted to cry when I first saw one of them come in, she is only eighteen, and had had a heart attack at university.

10.30am is time for snacks, a mug of coffee and a cereal bar, again we are watched by a nurse. People have been known to throw food out of the window when the nurse wasn't looking. I once saw a piece of blackened toast hanging off one of the tree branches.

11. o'clock is time for the first group, I have a different one every day in order Monday-Friday of: relaxation, self-esteem, assertiveness, community group and quiz. The groups are well run, useful, and are organised by the OTs. There are about three to fifteen in each group.

When the group finishes at 12.15 I go and have my pre-ordered meal. The average meal might be cannelloni, jacket potato and peas, followed by tinned peaches and custard. All the EDPs eat very slowly, cutting up their food very small. I used to have to cut croquette potatoes into six equal pieces. One girl once took individual grains of rice out of a curry and scraped the sauce off each of them. It was an absolute nightmare to watch. When you first come in you sit on the 'supervised table' i.e. two nurses sit with you to ensure you eat your meal. The people on the supervised table take up to an hour and a half to eat each meal. When I was there people would do anything to get rid of their food: hiding it up their sleeves, under their mats or cutting it up small and hiding it with sauce. The tricks they used were very crafty and used to constantly amaze me. The atmosphere is tense, but we are quite supportive and encourage each other.

It's 'supervision time' again until 1.30pm, with the same routine as before. People sit quietly doing crosswords or cross-stitch and there is little conversation. When people do talk it is mainly to analyse what people have/haven't eaten or hidden, and how they've behaved at mealtimes etc. and it is then discussed. People suffering from Eating Disorders frequently become withdrawn and depressed.

At 1.30pm I walk to the shop to buy *'Take a Break'* magazine or chewing gum, or I see an O.T. that's been assigned to me. We sit and talk about how things are going for me and general issues that need working on. If it gets too painful I sit and cross my arms while staring at the floor, not speaking. I have even been known to run out of the room. Eating Disorders are not simply about thin models in magazines but are extreme coping mechanisms used to cope with difficulties in people's lives. Anorexia and Bulimia are complicated mental illnesses and often arise when a person's life is changing or seems out of control in some way, thus dieting and purging become an area to regain control over.

At 2.00pm we have another group, again in order

Monday-Friday of relationships/goal setting group, yoga (Prana Yama) expressive group, yoga and creative group. Then 3.15pm is time for my snack of a mug of tea and an apple though recently I've allowed myself two sachets of sugar in my tea.

At 3.45pm I have another group, for three times a week it is (light) weights, of course the other EDPs can't do that as they don't weigh enough, we have a support group on Thursdays and stress management on Tuesdays. At 5pm I'll tidy my room before dinner at 5.30pm, which I usually finish at 6pm. I then sit in the evening lounge during supervision watching TV or writing letters. The supervised table comes in at about 6.45pm and there is always one of the girls in tears.

There are twelve of us EDPs in the hospital at the moment amongst a total of thirty five patients. One third are in for alcohol and drug addictions and a third for other mental health issues such as stress, anxiety or Obsessive-Compulsive disorder. Six of the EDPs are university students, three are graduates and three are married. There are no male EDPs here at the moment, as eating disorders tend to mainly affect women.

Seven o'clock is 'freedom time' for me when I have some hours to myself; sometimes there are visitors, more usually I'll phone my friends. I get very jealous hearing about what they're up to in the 'outside world'. However I am very lucky since my friends and family come and visit me a lot, some people's friends seem to 'vanish' when they become ill. I also watch TV, play music or do something creative such as painting. Some evenings I do written homework for my therapist. I once had to write an essay entitled: *'what I would do if I didn't have any fears'*. I'm careful when and how I do this work as it can bring up a lot of painful issues.

At nine I have a bath and read, it's *'Captain Corelli's Mandolin'* at the moment. Nine thirty is time for the final snack; I have a Horlicks and two digestives. There's one girl that breaks her biscuit into tiny crumbs and wipes it under her mug. This is difficult for me to watch because the anorexic side of me also wants to do such things. At ten I collect some more medication, have a white coffee, write my diary and fall asleep.

I have many hopes and dreams for the future, such as travelling around Asia, doing some photography and perhaps even one day learn to do parachute jumps. I see my time here as a massive learning curve, both about the world and myself. Hospital is a sort of 'university of life', though I hope to go to real university when I'm recovered.

Jasmine

If You Saw What I See

If you saw what I see
If you looked inside me
You would realise I am not what I seem.
The body cries yes, but the voices say no,
Then there's me lying trapped in between.

If you felt what I feel
Like the scars that won't heal
You would not want to be who I am.
All the pain that's inside me I just can't let out
Making believe I don't give a damn.

If you knew what I know
Like how far I can go,
You'd be shocked by my lies and deceit.
I'll do what I can, work so hard to betray you
– And not just about what I eat.

If you heard what I said
Right inside of my head
You'd be frightened and want to get out.
Away from the torment, the hate and the fear
The disgust, self-abuse and self-doubt.

If you saw what I see,
If you felt what I feel,
If you knew what I know,
If you heard what I said,

But you don't.

Jo

70

Inside Me

Inside my skin there's a space,
It twists and turns, it bleeds and aches.

Inside my head there's an empty room,
Its wanting, waiting, a need to be fulfilled.

A hunger, a starving, a bleeding desire
Frustrated, anxiety trapped and on fire.

I'm screaming inside and no one can hear
Because there is the rest of my being refusing to hear.

Tanya

My Heart and Mind

My heart is saying one thing
My mind is saying another,
This is just one problem
As I try to recover,

The food is in the kitchen
Only I am in the house
There's no way of stopping me
From consuming every ounce,

I hate myself for doing this
Always making myself vomit
For taking all the laxatives
I know I have to stop it;

I really have been trying
But I'm afraid to no avail,
All my work and effort
Seems always to fail,

I feel I have reached a point
Of knowing life's not fair,

Dear God, what you are doing to me,
Is really hard to bear.

Anonymous

My Stomach Hurts

My stomach hurts,
It's bloated and painful
I feel I've stuffed myself again,
Yet I could remove this pain,
                    this hurt

These...feelings
With the touch of two fingers
Tightening my stomach muscles
I know can bring relief;
A small hurt - so brief
Pain – but purgery:
This feeling will be gone.

'Hello Jan! Hello Helen! Hello Jenny!'
Those years don't feel too many,
I've invented a childhood with you,
A childhood that was stolen from me,
No life I create for myself
        Will ever be quite the same.

Now my heart hurts
Perhaps the alien stuff
Will evaporate with exercise?
How much should I eat?
I do not know,
Soft reassuring words must fall down about
                    me like snow.

Oh yes, I'm having such trouble today,
Can I swap places with you?
Just for one day?

Anonymous

Never Doing Enough

I'm not doing enough,
Not working enough,
Not caring enough.
Not enough.
Run, run, run, sprint, jog, dash,
Arm exercises, leg exercises. Sit ups.
Get rid of the cellulite.
I'm not doing enough,
Not learning enough.
Must do well in exams.
Everything must be perfect or I'm not.
Run. Run. Run.
Alcohol so I don't feel the pain.
My legs start to hurt – I'm so unfit
Just.
Another.
Mile.
Before.
I .
Can.
Quit.
Use those muscles. Use that brain.
You're such a waste – such a crying shame.
I'm not doing enough,
I haven't done enough.
Runningcryingscreamingsobbingshouting
Not doing enough. Not ever doing enough.

Anonymous

Only Harming Myself

It seems I'd rather be anywhere else but here.
First time in my double decade
I've seen out of the city an' across the hills.

Red stripes on arm are a badge of
                                    negative pride.
For the night I did that to me,
It seems the other Helen died.

Represent: don't touch or come too near
Look how hard I cut today.
(Silly when real life's all one fear)

Best thing I had today was a hug
Tears melting into warm smiles.
Strange how they accept what I see:
                    the unacceptable.

Helen

Parallel Worlds

In a parallel universe
She's now bringing up her breakfast,
In that place she'll drink a bottle of vodka tonight
And take the pot of tablets in the cupboard.
In a parallel universe
She's in a psychiatric ward bedroom
And someone sits on the chair outside
   –   in the parallel universe
Which has caused massive strife at home.

In the other world
She knows it's just the lack of sleep
And the food she ate is hers to keep.
In that parallel world
Amongst the stars shining bright
She phones her friends that keep her tight,
And the anchors holding her down
Ride through this windy storm.

In the parallel universe she shouts at the nurse,
Telling her to go away,
This damned self-fulfilling prophecy
Finally got its way.
The place where she tries to run away
Fights against the staff
Starts the long crawl upwards again.

In another world
She counts down days return to life - with glee.
Perfectionism doesn't ruin exams,
Nor the pressures of change:
She dances at nightclubs
Celebrating her birthday.

Anonymous

Perfection

Failing really scares me
I like to do my best,
I hate not being at the top
Coming second to the rest;

Sitting near the bottom
Where I don't want to be
I know I must retrieve myself
By doing well for me;

All that I can ever do
Is to give things a try,
Don't set myself targets
Which stand a mile high

*Because if I never reach them
Then this will get to me.*

Felicity

Punishment

So driven to be busy all of the time
Until those thoughts and feelings are left behind:
This is my crime.

Failing to do everything set,
Let us knit some hope into that heart of mine,
Only a computer screen to be met:
That was my crime.

The brakes have failed,
The bingeing starts such unfortunate actions
Only leaving eyes that smart:
That will be your crime.

A crime to love, a crime to care
Unforgettable incidents – and a cruel judge
Black conscience that cannot be fair,
Until only a small bright red heart,
                    Shiny and pure, is left to tear.

Sharon

Putting On Weight

Pain, indescribable pain,
To have to live and to have to gain.
Gram by gram, kilo by kilo,
I grow each day.

Lost in a hole, so dark and so deep,
Lonely and scared with nowhere to turn,
To be like others
Is a right I'll never earn.

When all I am is nothing,
With nothing to give,
An empty person,
With no strength to live.

All I cause is pain,
As I push people away,
But what else can I do,
When all they care is what I weigh?

Now they only come
When it's time for me to eat,
I'm all alone with my fears,
And my never ending tears.

No hope for tomorrow,
Or gladness for today,
Just more people I've made unhappy,
In the anorexic way.

But why won't they listen,
To how much I hurt,
Instead of making me eat,
Things I surely don't deserve?
Voices in my head,
That just won't go away,
A never ending battle,
With myself everyday.

Consumed by guilt,
I'm so confused,
Lost in depression,
From the world I'm removed.

Katy

Self-Destruction

So many times I destroy myself needlessly
With thoughts and doubts that should never be.
I destroy my pride, my self-respect, my confidence
Until nothing is left but a gaping hole
Where a person used to be.

I know so well that my misery is self-made,
Yet I cannot control the gradual decay of my dying soul.
My mind plays evil tricks on me,
It eats away slowly at the certainty,
Leaving only a huge mountain of doubt
Which haunts me day and night,
Increasing in strength minute by minute
Until it reaches the crazy heights of paranoia
And finally: crushes me...

Anne

Self-Harm

I can't go swimming
Sunbathe, or wear vest tops
Trademark rolling up of sleeves when thinking
Short sleeves when weather's hot.

Crop tops showing stripes along my stomach
Too criss-crossed, patchwork lace of scars.
So let this flesh show: beware cuts will be seen
Funny that unhappiness
Comes within the realms of pain,
Let the doctor say it's my fault
And there's no-one else to blame.

Anonymous

Sleepless Night

Sleeping, resting, calculating, digesting
No sleep, no rest, but
Calculate and digest.
Limitless energy anxiety driven,
No memories but pain and anger:
Mistakes eternally un-forgiven.

Spasmodic movement of limbs,
Working a hundred times each day,
Yet still I must do unending things,
Though from exercise I hesitate,
Bulimia shall not be my forever fate.

Genevieve

Splendid Existence?

Splendid existence forever unkind,
Forgive the heart to rehabilitate the mind,
Better this day to converse with friends
Than eat until sick,
Trying to make amends.
Can't be honest about how I feel,
I'm the one way far-out riddler
Integrity isn't revisited down the sink,
Thus, I forgive myself:
But what do you think?

Jasmine

The Appointment

You gaze at my facial expression
While I admire your shoes
And I spoke so softly that
Honesty had nothing to lose.

Didn't you feel frustrated
That I'd come so far then cut?
True: there's so many positives
Except the never-ending '*but...*'.

A bedroom search is frightening
No war-zone here 'cept mentally.
You versus me, me versus world
Us versus negativity.
Depression fighting back,
So rankled it changes tack:
'*Full speed ahead! To the end of the fall
no further: just then she could be dead.*'
Inside it's beautiful, from outside
It's blood I'm thieving.

Sharp pain has no long-term gain,
Except me versus you, us against it
Looking up I see you're still there
Winning patiently, and bit by bit.

Anonymous

The Battle of Feasting

There is no reason to cede the fight
Against this common enemy of ours.
Again and again she tests my strength
Savouring each morsel of flesh.

Now she sleeps in my bed
By day, tries on my clothes, but lets them
Slide off emasculated hips.

The distance between us was never far,
Now somehow into my personal space she slips
Dull cold eyes stare across me when feasting
Slowly she diminishes each slice to a slither,
With thin wet lips distended in a grimace
Off the white bony fingers slides grease and blood
Oiled with the bile of self-hate.
A concoction destined for bins, or worse,
                                    dank sewers.
Feeding off pain and death,
This figure is no more than skeletal,

All my honour was destroyed when osseous fingers
                        clutched at my heart;
Tightened the grip and squeezed out the love.

Only long corridors of forest green
Can destroy the power of this myth,
As the skeletal figure recedes into the distance
My heart is returned piece by piece.

Anonymous

The Deep End

Thrown in at the deep end
Unable to swim,
I wanted positive thoughts
But instead they were grim,

Instead of going forwards
I take another step back,
How much of this
Can I possibly hack?

I really want to sort things out
And change my life around
I know it takes a long time
To get your feet back on the ground;

But right now I want to get there
I know how hard it'll be
And from this horrible illness
I just want to be set free.

Leanne

The Outsider

I am standing at a window
Looking in at myself.
Living a life that is not mine,
And I wish I could change so many things.
But mostly I feel powerless,
Still knowing this must be the time for change.

I join in the laughter of others,
When really I see nothing funny,
And I do as others do
So I am not alone.
Too unsure of myself to be me
And too proud to be anything else.

I am living my life from the outside,
A stranger in my own world,
Waiting for someone to open the door
And let me in…
Or just searching in vain for the key.

Anne

Time for bed

I'm so tired,
And I have this whim:
Perhaps I'll go to bed in the clothes I'm in?
It seems only duvets of silk
Let me escape from the world,
I'll forget that extra glass of milk.
My defences are lowered,
Human senses appear deflowered:
If I write this down
It won't happen again,
And tomorrow I'll be in bed at a quarter to ten.
Days crammed with activity
Make me fear the future,
The fairies are calling me to lie down now
And awaken; an eye's wink more mature.

Jasmine

Tornado

Like a tornado,
Causing pain and destruction,
Everything is spinning,
Being turned upside down.

Not a tragic story on the news,
Just a nightmare all too true,
Darkness is upon us,
But where is the hope beyond the thunder?

When day is night,
And we think we're dreaming,
Then we can feel the tears come streaming,
And we are consumed again by fear.

Stuck in a ditch,
From where I can't climb out,
In a ring of hate,
My mind full of doubt.

How can anyone like me,
After all my illness has done?
And now they've given up on me,
And the evil anorexia's won.

Pushed away the people I love,
The only ones I live for,
Now I'm out on my own,
I really begin to suffer.

Alex

Selfless

I'll be what *you* want me to be,
Do what *you* wish of me.
Aim to cause *you* no negativity.

I'll try to make *you* happy
Don't worry for me, *your* priority.

If *you* hunger, take from me
I don't need it; I'm fine, no really!
Just be happy and well – for me?
There is no 'for me'
Because I'll be who *you* want me to be.

Tanya

Leanne's Story.

I didn't decide that I really wanted to recover from my eating disorder until I had been ill for three years. It meant I not only had to find a way to get better, but to come to terms with the roots of my anorexia. Thus, I read many books on the illness and became quite an expert. Now, at the age of eighteen, I have developed a number of long-term aims for my future, a future that I once didn't believe I might have. By writing this, I am able to share my experiences of comfort eating, followed by anorexia and bulimia to show that the severity of the illness is not always based on the weight of the patient.

I feel very lucky at the present time, as I have realised that by changing my life I can really start to live again. Until recently I felt so depressed I wasn't able to get up in the mornings, as there seemed no point. I wouldn't plan beyond the following few days, as I couldn't see that far in advance. Whilst suffering with an eating disorder life seems to lose its focus. The majority of your waking hours are consumed with thoughts of food, exercise, laxatives and calories.

It is sad to say that I almost felt guilty for living and I still feel guilt for having caused so much pain to those people that really love me. When I was ill, my self-esteem dropped to an all-time low and I couldn't understand why people were spending so much time on a 'useless' person such as me. Not only did I deprive myself of the nutrition that my body so desperately needed, but the love that was being given to me. I tried to push away anyone that showed me any love or affection. The eating disorder was not only killing me but my relationships with others and I lost a number of people close to me. However, despite my attempts to alienate myself, there were many who stuck close by.

I also used to get a voice inside my head, which I was too scared and embarrassed to tell anyone about. I kept this secret to myself, as I didn't want to be labelled as 'mad' or something even worse. What I didn't realise at this stage was that this voice was destroying me. It was the evil inside me telling me to do so many awful things. It is so important for people – especially the loved ones of those suffering with eating disorders – to understand this concept that some anorexics suffer from. The 'voice' – the anorexia must be separated from the person. I realise now for example, that it was not me telling my mum I hated her for trying to make me eat an apple, but the illness.

Everything I ate was a real struggle as one half of my head would tell me to eat it and the other half would tell me not to. The 'evil voice' as I now call it, made me do some really bizarre things. For example on the rare occasions that I did eat I had to make the food barely edible by covering it in vinegar or salt. Before eating the voice would say to me: *'you don't need to eat, you've already had a can of coke today. If you do have anything you'll get fat, as if you're not already fat enough!'.* During eating every bite would be a struggle as this is when the voice became the loudest. It would tell me to *'eat one bite then throw the rest away'.* Or *'eat any more and you will die and something awful will happen to your family'.* I would have to contend with the voice even after eating just a tomato or apple. The worst time was during a binge. Whilst eating it would be telling me to take as much food as possible, then when I stopped it would repeatedly tell me how selfish I was for eating it. Thus, after bingeing I would punish myself in a variety of ways such as by cutting myself, take excessive amounts of laxatives, exercise rigorously or even eating my own vomit.

These voices began when I was about ten, but back then it didn't dominate things, just tell me I was fat or lazy. Later, when it was at its worst it would tell me to cut myself or take an overdose. This voice I was unable not to give in to a few times, though thankfully I never did myself any long-term damage.

At the height of my anorexia I was almost permanently in a trance-like state. I would sit at school, staring out of the windows barely hearing what was going on around me. Often people would talk to me and I wouldn't respond, not because I was being rude or purposely ignoring them, but because the voices in my head were overpowering everything else. Going into a 'trance' was very frightening and for me I felt as if I was being alienated from society. Coming out of a trance was difficult and quite scary, and I needed a lot of love and encouragement.

Another problem for me was that I became an expert liar. I used a number of different tricks to avoid certain situations such as eating or going out. Sometimes I would even amaze myself by what I said. It is however, important to recognise that it wasn't really me that was saying these things but my anorexia. Over the years the voice became more sophisticated and this made me feel extremely selfish and deceitful. Being weighed was always a nightmare as I was petrified of being too thin and being admitted to hospital. To combat this I would drink vast quantities of water and wear heavy clothes so that I weighed more – though of course medical staff usually know all these tricks.

Depression was one of the hardest aspects of the eating disorder to cope with. I rarely looked forward to anything as simple tasks became really difficult. As my mood dropped it affected many different areas of my life. I slowly started to withdraw from as much social interaction as possible. I managed to 'put on a front' for a while until this became too hard to sustain. I tried so hard to appear 'normal'. When I went to school I literally had to 'play act' my day. If anyone at school mentioned food I would become instantly alert, afraid that they may be talking about me, and paranoid that they were aware something was wrong. Later I reached a stage when I did not care who knew about the eating disorder.

The distortion of my own body image was quite immense, though I wasn't aware of it at the time. I honestly believed that people were just telling me I was thin to make me feel better, or because they knew I was anorexic. Even when underweight I thought I was too fat. An anorexic person will constantly lower their body weight targets, and no weight ever seems low enough. At first I only wanted to lose half a stone, then a stone, and so it continued until I had lost dangerous amounts. Not surprisingly, this can do untold damage to your health, both long and short term. What is frightening is that the damage I was doing to my body and mind didn't bother me. I thought that I wasn't ill enough to have any of the physical problems that affect those who are acutely anorexic.

I was too busy worrying about whether my friends and family were OK, to ever think about my own well being. The personality of people with eating disorders is unique, they tend to be very caring and loving towards everyone, everyone that is but themselves. They tend to take on the worries of the family and beyond.

One thing that angers me greatly is the way the 'weight issue' is misrepresented by so many who talk about eating disorders. I have heard of many people who are seriously ill but haven't received the treatment they need because they haven't dropped below a certain weight. I was one of a minority to be admitted when not at a seriously low weight.

Going into hospital was extremely difficult. It is such a hard thing to have to 'put your life on hold' again. Once in hospital I discovered how important it is to challenge your negative thoughts and behaviours. Without this help and intervention there was no way I could make any progress. All I needed was for all the responsibility to be taken away from me and for people to give me a lot of support while eating. You have to relearn to have a normal relationship with food.

The idea of recovery used to be so hard for me to imagine. I knew that it was going to be a struggle. Finally though, I reached a stage where I really wanted to get better. I spent so much time helping other people, but at last I realised I needed to take some time for myself. I was putting my mind and body through so much and I don't think they could have taken it much longer. I remained so low for so very long until one day something just clicked.

When you are ill, you can't visualise life without an eating disorder. After all, it was my best friend and worst enemy for so long and I thought life would be empty without it. But at last I decided that it is not the sort of friend I want around me any more. Thankfully I've discovered that life without an eating disorder can be truly wonderful.

CHAPTER 3

Poems by and for Friends and Family

Feeble Mankind

'*The feeble one*' is me
'*The over sensitive one*' I'm known to be,
'*The sick one*', apparently,
'*The hopeless one*' – I wish they could see!
'*The strong one*' they seem to pull out of me,
'*You're worth it*', they scream to me,
'*You can do it*', transactional attitude is gifted to me.
'*Be you*', not what everyone expects of me.

Who am I?
But a feeble mankind.

Tanya

Guilt

Guilt.
When we go out together,
People staring at your tiny anorexic frame,
Do they think it's because of me?
Was it something I may have said,
Or done, or thought?
Didn't I ever say that you are enough as your are?
That God made no mistakes when He
Created you, you are just as you
Should be.
Guilt.
Because I want to help,
But feel powerless, and shut out, and ostracised,
On the sidelines of a mental game
You are fighting within yourself.
Guilt.
When I hear you making yourself sick,
And I want to batter down the door,
To stop you,
To stop you hurting yourself.
I'm worried sick.
Guilt.
When you cut yourself,
And I want to put a plaster over it,
Cuddle you like a child, and say
It will all be better.
Each cut hurts me too,
I write this at night, waiting, hoping,
Praying you will let me in,
So we can fight this together.

Judith

I Want to Change You

Your self-destruction cuts me down
With every agonising stroke,
The self-hatred and pain you feel,
The hurt which you contain.

I want to reach inside your heart,
Your mind,
To turn you round to see the beauty,
The beauty encasing your soul.

Your pain saddens me,
Your joy inspires me,
Your love helps my belief in myself to flourish.

The weapons that wound,
Each binge and each purge,
Short term relief from this life and this world.

Sometimes you're hollow and able to fade,
Destruction of mind and body, but never soul.

To be by your side is all I can do
I'm there with my love eternal for you.

Lauren

Isolation

Lonely.
And wandering through the rain
Relieving others' pain,
The noose tightens around the rose buds.
Tears start to roll down pallid cheeks
As the story is recounted for the second time;
Fumbling words that drop off into the receiver.

This fair girl so isolated
Prevents any heart coming nearer,
But the lifting of the mouthpiece from telephone
Represents a soul that will not die.
Somewhere deep inside she knows this is not the way,
Tiny errors are sins she feels she must pay.

Yet still the plea for help.
Is written artistically in a silken apology:
'I'm sorry that I feel,
Forgive these fears that feel so real'.

Grace

Lullaby

Goodnight sweet child
The future beckons you on
Winter's grasp has been so mild
And I'm here to lull you with this song.

I've seen everything my girl,
I was there with you today,
I feel your sorrow as problems unfurl
Does bingeing on chocolate make them go away?

Have faith my daughter,
Please keep strong,
If you have the will you can't go wrong.

So go to bed with a peaceful heart,
Sleep with a contented mind,
Each new day is a brand new start
So treat the inner-self with warmth and love
And the outcome will be kind.

Anonymous

Mother Dearest

What do I need to do
To have you love me too?
For you often get very mad,
Which makes me so sad:
I don't see you treat others this way
So why am I the one who has to pay?
I never seem to make you cheerful
It is because I am so sinful?
For the others make you smile
But for me I am on trial
You always talk behind my back
Knocking me straight off the track,
I wish that I could feel no pain
But I do, and go insane.
All those words haunt my thoughts,
For love can never just be bought,
Trust must be made
As my strength seems to fade,
How I wish you could read my mind
For there my struggles you will find,
I want you to help me
So that this trapped love can be set free.

Anonymous

Mum

Mum, you've stuck by me
Never left my side
Through all the hard times
Along the bumpy ride;

Slowly we will get there
With lots of support
I will make recovery
Which at times we never thought,

I know that I will make it
Although sometimes it's grim
But I have nearly realised
It's not worth it to be thin,

So many more important things
Including my own life
Which at so many different times
Had gone out of my sight.

How I would have I done it
Without all your love?
I don't think I would have made it
You're my gift from up above.

Leanne

My Daughter

When you were younger, you
Used to tell me when things were wrong,
My love is still there for you, but
Over the months
You have been slipping away,
Putting up walls and defences.

Where has my daughter gone?
The one whose laughter lit up the house,
Whose sense of humour sparkled on the edge
Of a character so strong.
You have always been tall, thin and beautiful,
Now that has gone,
Replaced by
Tears, anger and hatred.

And when I shout it's not because of
Anger, or disappointment, but fear,
Fear because I see you growing thinner and weaker,
And desperation:
I don't know what else to do.
It's been months since you ate with us,
Even more since you last smiled.
Where has my daughter gone?

Tricia

My Sister

They say my sister has an eating disorder,
'Cos she seems so thin,
And looks so sad, and lonely:
Her smile is so dim.
Yesterday I tried to hug her,
But was pushed away.
Last time I hugged her, I could feel her ribs,
She seems so fragile, like she could shatter if
I held her too strong.
Today I said I loved her,
And her face just turned away from me.

My sister borrows my clothes, 'cos hers
Don't fit her like they should.
At night I hear her tiptoe to the fridge,
Open the door and close it,
Several times a night.

Mum and Dad argue a lot now,
'Cos they don't know what to do,
Mum cries when she doesn't come to dinner,
I wish I could help her too.

Jessica

Our Secret Language

Code words. Safe food. Same body language.
She likes rice cakes too!
We think the same,
It's strange.
Perhaps she's an actress?
They've scripted the lines to make me talk.
The food's been placed down
       –   Even half-portions make me balk.
I have safe foods
Rice cakes, Ryvita, meat makes me retch.
Let these tears fall like raindrops
And nourish the hope under my feet.

I can't believe she knows my secret language.
If I have one biscuit I may as well finish the packet.
Haven't I blown it anyway?
At least: a whole packet means vomit more easily,
There's no way to rid such fears feasibly:
Except love, care, and encouragement,
You're just like us.
Come and join me at my table,
I won't see you trying to cut your food smaller than me:
Rise up won't you and shout that cry:
'Set me free, set me free'.

Jasmine

The Future is Yours

Nothing I can say can unburden
The weight of woes chaining
Your troubled spirit.
I confess,
No words I speak can unleash you from
That shadow haunting your days and nights.
Your winter of discontent.

Yet you must know
That I too had a shadow,
Which overcame me,
And like a parasite,
Sucked away my confidence,
Deprived me of nutrition.

A temporary disruption to this cycle of life.

Now I stand resolute, convinced of my worth,
Secure, self-assured,
Filled with contentment.
For after war comes peace,
Emancipation, and independence.

It shall be yours.

Shona

The Girl across the Room

You walk into the room,
I can see from a mile off
That your hips poking out
Are more than just bones showing through,
But distress and unhappiness.

How I wish I could
Transplant all that is in my head,
All that I learned and went through,
To make you better, to say
It doesn't have to be like this,
To save you the pain.

You say you're fine,
I know the truth.

My life has been the happiest ever
Since I recovered:
That is what I would say,
        If I could,
If you were able to listen,
If you were ready to hear.
That life without the illness is better than
Life before it all began.

I'm waiting, when you are ready.

Jasmine

Things I Need

Mum, I love you so
For all the things you do and know,
Although I often struggle
With the things you juggle
For in our personalities we do differ,
And so I must loosen up and not get stiffer.
For you offer such a lot
And I have to say
That I do love you more today
But still more work is to be made
So what we do have will not fade
But help from you I truly need
So love and trust my mind can feed,
For these are the things I feel aren't there
So the pain you want to hear, I cannot bear.

Anonymous

Try to Let Go

Try to let go
Begin to free your past
I don't want to say goodbye
This time has gone too fast;

The sadness inside you
Has consumed your entire mind,
But I know that the secrets
Are hidden deep down inside:

A little bit of courage
If only a small piece
Can hopefully just free you
From the deadly crazy beast

See the view in the mirror
Yes, that's really you
A beautiful strong person
Who can play the game of life too.

See the heart within you
Begin to feel again
We'll be here to support you
And save all this pain.

Naki

Andrew's Story.

It's getting better, but there still exists the misconception that 'Men do not suffer from Eating Disorders', or even: 'Men who have Eating Disorders must be suffering from something different to women who suffer from Eating Disorders'.

I did not realise throughout my childhood what was happening to me, I just thought I was not allowed to eat. I felt ashamed and guilty about eating. In retrospect, I can now see what was happening how I had a chronically low self-esteem then, and how it deteriorated. There were many times when I denied having a problem. As childhood progressed to adulthood I buried my feelings, throwing myself into work and a whole host of other things. I was trying to achieve perfection and provide for others in a world I felt ashamed to exist in: I had to justify my existence.

Then life took a turn. My self-esteem was blown away; a few comments and actions of others undid all that I had been doing to stay positive. Overnight I lost my 'cloak' and my negative mind was in control. I realised that I was on a slippery slope, but I thought I could handle it. I fought to get myself better:

I can do it myself. Do not bother others with your need for help'.

Yet months dragged on, and nothing improved. I promised myself that if I was not better by a certain date I would hold my hands up and go to my GP. That date arrived, I was in hospital three days later.

I felt shrouded in shame at what people might think or say. Of course, people said things like '*But... You're male?*' or: '*I didn't know men could develop Anorexia*'. All these things drove me deeper in the belief that I had done something wrong, and that I did not deserve to exist.

Treatment was started, and I soon came to learn that, in essence, there is no difference between men and women suffering from an Eating Disorder. A low self-esteem is frequently apparent for both. Sometimes it is related to sporting physique, but it's not limited to that. Some research I've read said that there is a higher incidence of gay men suffering with an Eating Disorder. Apart from that, there is little difference in the causes of men and women suffering an Eating Disorder.

Unfortunately men have been less likely to confess to suffering from an eating disorders, so the myth continues that men do not suffer. My psychiatrist said that around one in ten people suffering from an Eating Disorder are male. I think the figure is probably higher.

My treatment first concentrated on getting me to accept treatment – and take myself out of denial. The process of re-feeding and exploration of underlying causes was intensely painful. I likened my eating disorder to a polar ice cap: on top was the thick layer of ice (my eating disorder), and underneath the ice was water (all my emotions and feelings). As holes were made in the ice, the pressure of the water underneath gushed up through the tiny holes, which I would then plug up: it was too painful to expose the feelings.

At the lowest depth of my treatment, I wrote about

how I felt. Here is an extract from that time:

'When first I felt unable to eat, I thought it was a passing moment of sadness at a time I found hard to accept. However it grew within me into the immense self-hatred I have for myself today. On the one hand people cannot understand the problem – and on the other – I feel that they do not understand me. Now I feel totally devoid of self-worth. Oh, how I hate myself! Maybe that deep down I know that I have reached rock bottom, and the only way now is up? But how do I lift this ten-ton brick that has me pinned down? Nobody touches me anymore. I must be a leper. Are they scared at the ferocity of my illness? I certainly am.

On a practical level, where am I now? Unable to eat. Scared of uncleanliness. Scared of taking food (it's stealing). Scared to cry, scared to smile, scared to show any emotion. Destroyed by a world that thinks I am undesirable. Unable to work and look after myself in a way which others previously called fastidious. Now look: total disarray, confused by the messages the world sends me.

There are many nights of tears and distress. Locked up and incarcerated within myself, further diminishing my self worth and justification to exist, but not allowed to die. You owe to others to live – but not to exist.

Lonely in a world screaming at me to disappear into a corner hidden from all – yet still expected to be there. So long as I am there – okay, so long as I do not make myself known – okay. Realisation of emotions leads to greater feelings of worthlessness'.

Many months of Cognitive Behaviour therapy and group counselling were used to undo this low self-esteem. Essentially we had to undo all the suppressed negative feelings that stretched far back into early childhood. My family and friends became more able to accept that men can suffer from eating disorders. There was nothing vastly different about me from any of the other patients receiving treatment.

Perseverance – sticking to a prescribed diet, staying with emotions when they came up; tackling them, acknowledging them, dealing with them; and then adjusting self image all had to be faced. It was hardly ever easy, and many times there were slips back into old modes of behaviour. But I kept facing in the right direction. There was a goal I was heading towards and I was determined to get there.

It took a year of intensive treatment to get there. And when I got there, life was what I had never known before, a happiness and contentment with myself I had never known before. Life was, I found out, for living and enjoying, without the need to feel resentful of my existence.

I cannot deny the future for me may always hold the threat of my eating disorder returning. I do, however, now know how to send my negative mind away.

Andrew

CHAPTER 4

Recovery

Accepting Again

I want to accept myself:
Tonight, this day, tomorrow,
And forever,
For then I can turn this around,
And start putting my life together.

Anonymous

Archways

I see the archways before me
Yet I press the screen against my face: -
More aware of the sun's damage
                              Than its beauty.
I long to be back amongst the foliage,
Weaving and ducking my way through ivy.
My book told me to take such a path,
No matter what my age or temperament.
Message in a bottle, voices sent from God.
Did you hear about the creature (not far from here)
Who grew wings because he believed he could fly?
Too perfect to be untrue!
My, oh my, what a wonderful day!

I see the archways, now I see them:
In my eyes they are made of gold
Because they represent the name of blessed opportunity
And something so much more than that,
Something so much more,
I never, ever, wish for my land to be flat.

Anonymous

Beginning Again

Each time I eat my allotted meal
I improve my quality of life,
Easing this mental strife,
There's living to be done beyond
Eating disorder or; *'food, that big deal'*.

Every time I refuse to cut
My skin's healed together with
This mind, for now I truly live
Thus innumerable doors are opened
When the one with razors is shut.

Apparently the anti-depressants are crutches
How nice to throw them down the well
Escape from prolonged self-torture hell,
Walk unaided upright and strong
Freedom's light-hearted, away from a world of wrong.

Jasmine

Dark Hand of Fate

Release me dark hand of fate
That abandons me in here;
To make me wait.

Once thinking I learned my lessons
But returned with unreasonable anger,
Crying from cutting and chemicals
Bite the hand that tries to help
Questioning this world and myself
Confusion of feelings denied
Shameful mélange of emotions
Only she can help, just this last time;
Never did the night seem more despairing
Gloomy eyes of fate are glaring
Nothing will cure, though the cuts plead.
Inside the glass globe
Into others' brains I probe,
To discover hate for me within
Skeletal girls are more than this.
Release me dark hand of fate.

Release me dark claws of fate
Let me learn the lesson
That's not too late
Alone and agitated,
Relieve and heal,
Promise me, never again.

Anonymous

123

Fighting On and Up

Because I'm fighting
I'm truly fighting
And as I write these words
The hope is to save others
From this and worse.
Should it bring inspiration to
Two people or hundreds
Be appreciated by one soul?
Indeed it was worth it.
For now I must imagine
A helping hand to reach right out
Giving me more strength
Than I thought could ever be allowed.

Checking out the reality,
Chucking out the negative
Then holding the positive tight inside
Drying up the tears I've cried.
This once I've stopped looking to the past for inspiration
Believing that the road's no longer looped
Back and forth, new day, new course.

Such fears – relatively small
Yet I turn to the thinner door
The one that punishes
Then begs this body for more.
My dream last night
Involved so much cutting pain
Each lasting reminder of sin
Of efforts dying in vain.

Here's not where I want to be:
Plain to see
Clear to me.

Anonymous

Glimmer of Hope

At last I can say
An end's come into sight
Stuck in the tunnel
There's a glimmer of light,

Whatever it takes
I'm willing to do
It'll take time
But I'm sure I'll pull through.

The promises I've made
I know that I'll keep
There is a new life there
Which I'm looking to seek:

A world full of hopes
And new found dreams
Life's so amazing,
Or that's how it seems.

For such a long time now
Everything's been on hold
It's like seeking the treasure
And finding the gold.

Leanne

Goodbye Anorexia

Goodbye anorexia.
I want you no more,
I no longer need you
For what you were there for.
I know that you were there for me
In good times and in bad,
You sometimes made me happy
But more often made me sad.

Goodbye anorexia.
After all these years
It has taken so much time
But I no longer need you here
You were my way of coping
With so many different things:
But now I want to enjoy
Whatever my life might bring.

Julia

Goodbye

Oh dearest friend, who's been with me
Through every night and day,
Constant companion that I need
To keep life's troubles at bay.

And yet I've come to realise
(Though it's made me scream and cry)
That I'd be better off by far
If I could only say 'goodbye'

I really can't imagine life
Without you there to reign,
You showed me self-control supreme,
And blocked out all my pain.

But in return you took my health,
My muscles next to useless,
You forced me to leave college too,
You've been so completely ruthless.

You made me lose my self-confidence,
And leave my friends behind,
Manipulate my family
Who've always been so kind.

Through all of this I've loved you,
But now I must be strong
Since you've left me nearly dead
I have to say: 'So long'.

Fiona

Hope

Where am I going, am I getting well,
Have I found an escape from that lonesome living hell?
It's been years of isolation, years without belief,
A journey of self-destruction, bringing much
                                      pain and grief.
I was pursuing a path with my mind's eye:
Didn't know my perception was wrong
Till I looked up and saw death was approaching
      – And I knew I could not carry on.
I could see a light in the distance,
And I could feel the heat of the fire,
I felt frightened and started to falter,
Weak and weary I started to tire.

So I fell to my knees, put my hands in the air,
I accepted that I don't know best
And I opened my heart to the people that care
I found a safe place where at last I could rest.
It was a scary and humbling decision
To ignore my own well known voice
But it freed me from an evil prison:
Once released it gave me back choice.
Day by day I grow more strong and steady
And, though I still need much help to survive
I owe my life to all who've stood by me
Thanks to them, today I'm alive.

Alex

129

Human Fortress

'Twas the greatest battle
I've ever had to fight.
An elusive cunning enemy: Anorexia.
The hardest battles are those created within,
The only barriers are those you construct yourself,
Every day,
Year by year.

Fences turn to imposing walls,
A fortress built of shame and melancholy,
Deprived of food,
Starved within,
Laid to siege by its own mind.

It took an army of medical staff to stop
The self-made siege,
We won the battle together.

Now freed, I stand taller, stronger,
Than any battlements could.
Strength from deep inside,
Ready to grasp life with both hands,
Prepared to overcome all hurdles.
They seem smaller than before.

The siege was ineffective.
Friends now say I'm the happiest crusader they've
known.
They're right.

Fortresses remain bound to the ground,
The same spot and place in time,
Unable to evolve and grow as
A young woman should,
Cold, hard, devoid of curves,
The walls limited my dreams.

Now I've broken free,
Found my liberty,
I've travelled, traversed the world
And its many seas. Made foreign friends.

The hardest battles aren't those on the outside,
But the ones we fight within.

Jasmine

I Will Not Let It Defeat Me

Little bells toll the simple truth:
I will not let it defeat me.
One blip of time
In a myriad of evenings
I'm no longer scared of you:
I'm scared of me,
Me, and the lonely iron hands ready to grab
                    at each corner
Why today? Why tonight?
Losing that opportunity to shine
Pushed me onto the door labelled
             'Put up a fight'.

I see gold and white elephants serenading,
You see dark shapes of vultures circling,
Snatches of lyrics run through my brain
Encapsulating the thought
      'Things can never be the same'.

Jasmine

Invincible? Not I

A belief that thin was beautiful
That beauty was perfection,
That only perfection could succeed.

Empty of true feelings, empty inside,
Safe and secure, protected from reality.

Oh what beauty I could only see
Thinner and purer, paler and weaker.
....
But know I see though illusions,
Invincible? Not I.
That desire to be beautiful, lost in ignorance
Thin is not beauty, thin is the scars and pain.

Because of that belief, a broken body exists
Never will change bring perfection.
Perfection could have been – if left well alone
Now is the time to learn, to accept what I am,
who I am,

My body is my friend; it is broken and scarred,
But now I must remember that
My friends can't be perfect.

Joanne

It's Time to Say Goodbye

Somewhere deep inside of me
Something's got a hold of me
That's pushing me and everyone else away:
And I don't know why.

I just keep saying everything's fine:
When really it's eating me up inside,
I can see everybody else's pain but not my own:
And I don't know why.

It will cause me pain to end this relationship
It's been with me for so very long,
But I know I have to do it now
For I don't want it any more
And, for the first time ever,
I know why.

Jenny

My Eating Disorder

For most eating and drinking is just a way of life,
For me it is a symbol, an expression of strife.

I judge myself by everything that enters my mouth.
I think of food a lot, like my East, West, North and
South.

Everything in my head revolves around food and drink.
Everything is telling me to stop.
Don't eat. Think.

Think about what eating does to you in every way.
Think of it inside you, sitting there all day.

Of course I know it's silly, you have to eat to live
If I gained so much as a pound though,
                                        myself I'd never forgive.

As time goes on I know I need to beat this illness.
As I hate the life it has created, not a life, a mess.

I've felt the fears before. I hope I'll succeed again.
I want free of anorexia and one that's free from pain.

Gemma

Now I'm Free

You wouldn't spot me as 'one of them'
If I stepped onto the bus,
Wandered the supermarket aisles,
Or ate in a restaurant.
I wear catsuits now,
Instead of baggy jumpers and kids' trousers,
And laugh, dance and write.
I'd be lying if I said it didn't change me:
It has,
Each time I see the scars
I remember how much there is to live for,
Life is just growing, beginning, burgeoning, blossoming,
My awareness is enhanced now,
Each unhappy looking girl
Scouring the nutritional column for fat
Saddens me.

The illness changed my life:
Changed it for the better.
You wouldn't notice me now
Buying coke and crisps at the bar,
'Cos I've been to hell and back,
and somewhere in between.

Now I know who I am: a fighter
Welcoming this gift of life and all its wrappings.
The future is brighter than the past ever was,
Or could have been.

Hell taught me many things,
As did the recovery in between.

Sophie

Theatre of Life

A role was created: for me alone.

Demanding, difficult, definitely rewarding.
No-one else can fulfil it
                Quite like me,
The part can't be played by a skeleton,
It needs vigour and vitality.

Written for me, directed by God.

So I sacked the skeleton:
It wasn't part of the cast,
Wasn't needed, wasn't wanted, wasn't useful.

It is spring on stage now for me,
The backdrop shines brightly,
The skeleton is redundant.

Amelia

The Mountain Top

Once I said
The illness had ruined my life.
I was wrong.

Some gifts come in the strangest packages,
'Cos not every lesson is learned in the classroom.
Not every achievement can be inscribed on a C.V,
I had to climb to the top of the treacherous mountain,
To discover the wonderful views.

Recovery was a bitter path,
Yet,
Now I'm truly alive
This heart lies lighter than before,
My confidence has returned times four.

The mountain track was rough and cruel,
And worth every painful, shaky step.

Shona

Tomorrow

When all is gone
And there's no-one there,
I just turn to you
And I know you care.
Through thick and thin
We have been
So many things
We have seen so much.

A shining star
In the darkened night,
At the end of the tunnel
A glimmer of light,
That is just you
Through and through –
But only descend
On a certain few.

For all of the good
You're twice as bad,
For all of the happy
You're twice as sad,
So that is why
The time has come,
To say goodbye
And just be done.

I'll try and go on
And do my best,
But whether I do
That is the test.
A mind that is racing
A heart full of sorrow
I'll begin to move on,
And search for tomorrow.

Lucy

Recovery

Recovery is hard and long,
A battle all the time
Struggling to eat the meals
That are keeping me alive;

Without the pressure from people
I wouldn't be here now
Long ago I'd have given up
Not given life a go.

But now I'm feeling positive
Waiting to reclaim my life
Finding a reason for my existence
Now an end's come into sight,

I must take each day at a time
And always keep my chin up
I know I must remember
Not to dwell on every hiccup.

Charlotte

Perception

If I hadn't been ill,
I wouldn't be the person I am now,
Aware of my courage and beauty, perhaps
I would still be oblivious to the love surrounding me,
(Though it had to be shown through parents' tears,
And friends' pleas.)
I wouldn't know how to meditate,
Or how to send the blues away, perhaps
I would still be fearful where
Now there lies faith,
Insecure, where now there shines optimism.
Today my health must come first,
For without my body I have nothing,
And my happiness has priority over the
Rat race, the difficulties, the lies and the fears.
Now I am happy within,
So they can say what they like, think what they will,
I am here; I am me, happy within.

Tracy

Two Voices

I'm faced with a dilemma:
Two different voices in my head
One tells me not to listen
To what the other one has said;

One preaches about recovery,
And aiming for my goals
The other tells how fat I am
And throws me down the holes;

I wish the anorexic voice would go
And leave me to recover,
Because out there is a happier life
Which I want to discover.

Anonymous

Unfettered Hopes and Dreams

What is the unfettered dream?
It's about self-love and respect,
Real confidence and self-esteem,
Accepted worthiness
Of life existence itself:
Participating within the world,
Not me with food upon the shelf.

I discovered that while travelling
Some food fears were overcome;
So terrifying and not the easiest thing,
Greasy burgers and fries on ferry,
Hot dogs in Amsterdam made us merry,
Ice-creams in Prague, Venice and Rome,
With croissants in Paris I felt really at home.

So I lapse into standard form
Double line spacing, Times New Roman twelve;
Ending the E.D. needn't be so forlorn.

Nathalie

Lorna's Story

December, I am thirteen years old. I sit in my room in a huddle on the floor whilst tears stream down my face. The door is blocked off with a chair and numerous pieces of clothing. My mum pleads with me to open the door, but I don't listen to her, I can't hear her, my head is just too full of words and the words keep tumbling through my mind. My new psychiatrist claims I have *that illness*. But I haven't, I can't do. All I want to do is lose weight. It's no big deal, and I'm so fat, I can't stop now.

'*Why won't everyone just go away?*'

I feel incredibly angry, but most of all frightened. I can't believe this, it can't be happening.

That autumn and Christmas were the worst in my whole life. 'A Visit to Hell' is the only way I can describe that period of time. I seemed to go round in a circle. Not eat. Eat a bit. Cut myself. Not eat. Eat a bit. Cut myself. It wasn't pleasant, in fact it was indescribably horrible. Imagine how it feels to wake up in the morning and all you can think about is food? The calorie content, the way it controls the way you look, the way it controls the way you think, the taste, the texture, the fat content - everything! I woke up thinking of food, sat in class thinking of food, and went to sleep thinking of food. I even dreamed about food. I hated it, and yet I had a complete obsession with the stuff.

No doubt people were worried about me. I wouldn't talk much, although I enjoyed cooking for others and putting yoghurt in my friends' mouths. I looked at the calorie content of their food and made a mental note of how many calories they were consuming daily. It made me happy to think I was eating half of what they were eating. It gave me a feeling of relief, almost like butterflies in my stomach.

On first of January I wrote in my diary that one goal this year was to get rid of my anorexia. It seems I had come to the realisation that I had the disease by then. But the frightening thing was, one side of me was screaming for help, wanting to get out, wanting to be normal, while the other side controlled me completely. It told me I was 'fat and disgusting' and that I would be 'special' if I lost weight.

Here is an extract from my diary I was writing at the time: a lot of the things I wrote are so personal to me it is hard to share them. But what I can share is the general feeling of how I felt then:

January 11th

Hi – I haven't eaten anything today so I feel kind of weak. It's a punishment though. If I eat over my amount I have set myself then I won't eat anything for a few days. Simple as that.

January 12th

I cut myself earlier on and it really hurts. I was going to eat a little tomorrow but now I don't want to as I was told off for leaving on the lights. I don't deserve anything.

In March I was still seeing my psychiatrist and having outpatient treatment. Yet he knew, and I knew, it wasn't working. So on the tenth of March I was admitted into a special eating disorders hospital in the south of England.

The first day was so incredibly scary. I sat in my room with Mum and Dad. One of the nurses came up to me and asked me if I liked cheese. My automatic response was 'no'. She asked me if I liked cheese and pickle and even though I said I wasn't hungry she brought me a cheese sandwich. I can still now identify with that feeling of complete panic and anger. The anorexia was really in control and was angry with what was happening, angry with me.

When I first met the other girls on my unit I was shocked and horrified. I wanted to break down in tears when I saw the state they were in. They looked so thin, their arms were just emaciated, skin with their bones poking through. Their skin hung off their face and body, and they all had wide eyes that showed fear. I was surprised because there were only three other eating disorder patients on my ward apart from me.

After being weighed, I was led to the lounge for 'snacks'. This included two Hobnob biscuits, with a drink of water. It was so awful and I had such an urge to throw up. But there was little chance of that – my bathroom was locked. After snacks I was just going to leave the lounge when one of the girls came up to me and told me she was here for me if I ever needed any help. Then she looked at me and gave me a hug. The other two girls did the same. I was so choked. Here I was petrified, while I was being treated so nicely, I think that's when I realised I wasn't alone.

One major problem I had been having for a while was with the amount of water I was supposed to have, and for a while I had this crazy thought that if I didn't drink I would lose weight. So the second day I was there, it wasn't surprising I fainted in the hall. I was rushed to my room in a wheelchair, which actually was pretty cool, as they whizzed me down that hall fast. I was put on my bed and was able to rest.

A lot of my stay at the hospital was scary. As I put on weight, things became easier and the staff were eventually able to trust me to have the bathroom unlocked, and let me go out for longer walks in the grounds. I'm not going to tell you that treatment was easy, because frankly it wasn't. Contrary to the popular image of an eating disorder patient, I didn't just sit in bed each day as they fed me up. Each day we had a program and we had different groups. I found that the more honest I was in the groups I had to go to, the easier the concept of the illness became. We dealt with a lot of feelings that we never thought could be touched upon, and we went really deep into ourselves. I dealt with a lot of reasons why I became anorexic: I had been emotionally bullied, and had problems around death in the family that I felt unable to deal with. I also was physically developing and couldn't accept this at all. I preferred the more boyish figure with no breasts, and no bum. Plus, I hated having my periods and looked up to wafer-thin supermodels.

I was in hospital from March to the end of May. I missed school, but I was mainly relieved, as I didn't enjoy it anyway. I dealt with a lot of issues with the help of the girls in my group and my therapist. The eating became easier, and as I made more progress emotionally the anorexia became easier to deal with. Perhaps I make it sound like it was simple? But it wasn't, and that's what a lot of anorexics find so hard. The fact is, at the end of the day, you've got to make the decision. Do you want to get better or not? Your answer decides where you go from there.

I returned to school in September, and I admit it was difficult. Memories of my past experiences came up, I still had a problem with my body image, but I was at a healthy weight for my height. I dealt with the feelings of my body weight from the start of treatment. At the time of writing I continue to go back to the hospital every Saturday. I also have a group at the hospital, which really helps. I have a menu plan I follow, and I've learnt how to deal with the anorexia striking back at me. At last, I am ready to begin life again.

Useful Addresses:

The Eating Disorders Association
First Floor Wensum House
103 Prince of Wales Road
Norwich
Norfolk
NR1 1DW
Helpline: (01603) 621 414
Youthline: (0845) 634 7650

Childline: 0800 11 11

The Samaritans: 08457 909090

Mind:
15-18 Broadway
London
E15 4BQ
Helpline: (0845) 766 0163

National Self-Harm Network
PO Box 16190, London, NW1 3WW

Entries correct at time of print